A New Tune
for Clarinet

The clarinet edition of *A New Tune A Day* is designed to be used seamlessly with the saxophone edition.

Teachers wishing to accommodate both instruments in a lesson will be able to do so with almost every piece of every lesson, including the duets and rounds, except where indicated: look for this symbol within the book ✳

The useful addition of chord symbols in the concert key for many of the pieces in this book will enable the teacher to provide an accompaniment on guitar or piano.

Boston Music Company
part of The Music Sales Group
London/New York/Paris/Sydney/Copenhagen/Berlin/Madrid/Tokyo

Foreword

Since its appearance in the early 1930s, C. Paul Herfurth's original *A Tune A Day* series has become the most popular instrumental teaching method of all time. Countless music students have been set on their path by the clear, familiar, proven material, and the logical, sensibly-paced progression through the lessons within the book.

The teacher will find that the new books have been meticulously rewritten by experienced teachers: instrumental techniques and practices have been updated and the musical content has been completely overhauled.

The student will find clearly-presented, uncluttered material, with familiar tunes and a gentle introduction to the theoretical aspects of music. The books are now accompanied by audio CDs of examples and backing tracks to help the student develop a sense of rhythm, intonation and performance at an early stage.

As in the original books, tests are given following every five lessons. Teachers are encouraged to present these as an opportunity to ensure that the student has a good overview of the information studied up to this point.

The following extract from the foreword to the original edition remains as true today as the day it was written:

The value of learning to count aloud from the very beginning cannot be over-estimated. Only in this way can a pupil sense rhythm. Rhythm, one of the most essential elements of music, and usually conspicuous by its absence in amateur ensemble playing, is emphasised throughout.

Eventual success in mastering the instrument depends on regular and careful application to its technical demands. Daily practice should not extend beyond the limits of the player's physical endurance — the aim should be the gradual development of tone control alongside assured finger-work.

Music-making is a lifelong pleasure, and at its heart is a solid understanding of the principles of sound production and music theory. These books are designed to accompany the student on these crucial first steps: the rewards for study and practice are immediate and lasting.

Welcome to the world of music!

Sincere thanks to Matt Hunt for his invaluable help with this book.

Published by
Boston Music Company

Exclusive Distributors:
Music Sales Limited
14-15 Berners Street, London W1T 3LJ, UK.
Music Sales Corporation
257 Park Avenue South, New York, NY 10010, USA.
Music Sales Pty Limited
20 Resolution Drive, Caringbah, NSW 2229, Australia.

This book © Copyright 2005 & 2006 Boston Music Company,
a division of Music Sales Limited
Revised 2006

Edited by David Harrison
Music processed by Paul Ewers Music Design
Original compositions and arrangements by Sarah Pope and Janet Coles
Cover and book designed by Chloë Alexander
Photography by Matthew Ward
Models: Joshua Williams and Lizzie Frost
Printed in the EU
Backing tracks by Guy Dagul
CD performance by Matt Hunt
CD recorded, mixed and mastered by Jonas Persson and John Rose

Your Guarantee of Quality
As publishers, we strive to produce every book to the highest commercial
standards. The music has been freshly engraved and the book has been
carefully designed to minimise awkward page turns and to make playing
from it a real pleasure. Throughout, the printing and binding have been
planned to ensure a sturdy, attractive publication which should give years
of enjoyment. If your copy fails to meet our high standards, please inform
us and we will gladly replace it.

www.musicsales.com

Contents

Rudiments of music

The stave

Music is written on a grid of five lines called a *stave*.

At the beginning of each stave is placed a special symbol called a *clef* to describe the approximate range of the instrument for which the music is written.

This example shows a *treble clef*, generally used for melody instruments.

The stave is divided into equal sections of time, called *bars* or *measures*, by *barlines*.

Note values

Different symbols are used to show the time value of *notes*, and each *note value* has an equivalent symbol for a rest, representing silence.

The **quaver** (or *eighth note*), often used to signify a half beat, is written with a solid head and a stem with a tail. The quaver rest is also shown.

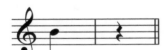

The **crotchet** (or *quarter note*), often used to signify one beat, is written with a solid head and a stem. The crotchet rest is also shown.

The **minim** (or *half note*) is worth two crotchets. It is written with a hollow head and a stem. The minim rest is placed on the middle line.

The **semibreve** (or *whole note*) is worth two minims. It is written with a hollow head. The semibreve rest hangs from the fourth line.

Other note values

Note values can be increased by half by adding a dot after the note head. Here a minim and a crotchet are together worth a *dotted* minim.

Grouping quavers

Where two or more quavers follow each other, they can be joined by a *beam* from stem to stem.

Time signatures

The number of beats in a bar is determined by the *time signature*, a pair of numbers placed after the clef.
The upper number shows how many beats each bar contains, whilst the lower number indicates what kind of note value
is used to represent a single beat. This lower number is a fraction of a semibreve so that 4 represents crotchets
and 8 represents quavers.

𝄴, for *common time*, is
another way to write $\frac{4}{4}$.

$\frac{6}{8}$ means six quavers to the bar.

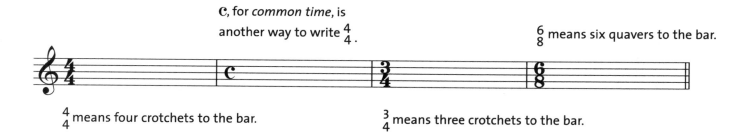

$\frac{4}{4}$ means four crotchets to the bar.

$\frac{3}{4}$ means three crotchets to the bar.

Note names

Notes are named after the first seven letters of the alphabet and are written on lines or spaces on the stave,
according to pitch.

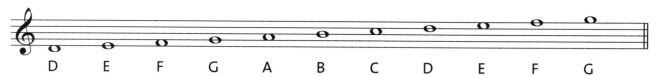

D E F G A B C D E F G

Accidentals

The pitch of a note can be altered up or down a half step (or *semitone*) by the use of sharp and flat symbols.
These temporary pitch changes are known as accidentals.

The *sharp* (♯) raises the pitch of a note.

The *natural* (♮) returns the note to its original pitch.

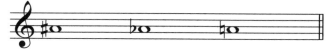

The *flat* (♭) lowers the pitch of a note.

Ledger lines

Ledger lines are used to extend the range of the stave for low or high notes.

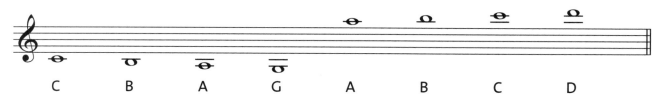

C B A G A B C D

Bar lines

Various different types of bar lines are used:

Double bar lines divide one section of music from another.

Final bar lines show the end of a piece of music.

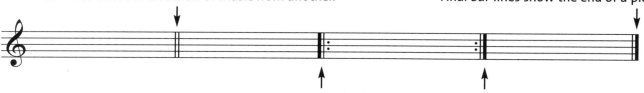

Repeat marks show a section to be repeated.

Before you play:

The clarinet and accessories Your complete clarinet outfit should include the following:

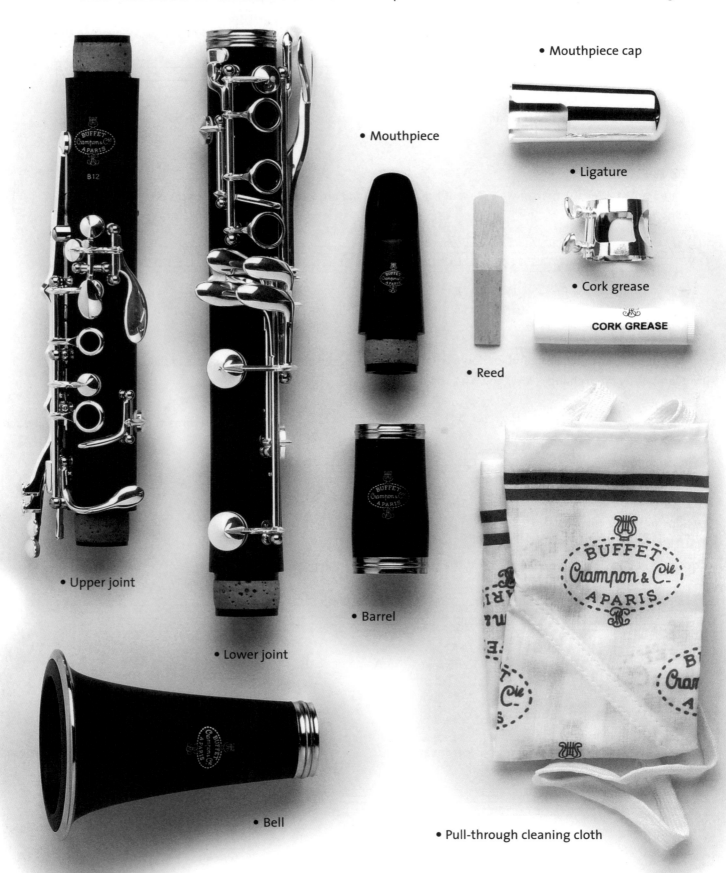

• Mouthpiece cap

• Mouthpiece

• Ligature

• Cork grease

• Reed

• Upper joint

• Barrel

• Lower joint

• Bell

• Pull-through cleaning cloth

Setting up routine

1. Select a reed that is clean and undamaged (they are quite delicate); place the reed on your tongue, close your mouth and swirl saliva around the reed to moisten it.

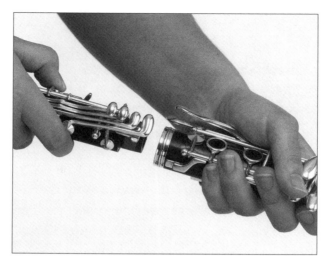

It's important to make sure that the reed is good and moist before you begin to play.

2. While you are moistening the reed, connect the upper and lower joints using a *twisting* action. As you do this, push the lower of the two rings on the upper joint down to raise the top half of the linkage over the bottom half. Use this linkage to check the alignment of the joints.

3. Twist on the bell, the barrel and finally the mouthpiece.

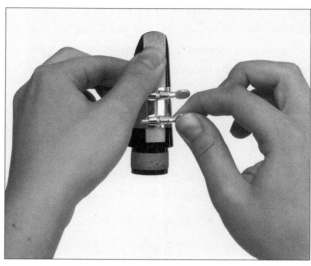

The ligature should be tight enough to hold the reed firmly. When you've finished playing remove the reed and wipe off excess moisture before replacing it on the mouthpiece.

4. Attach the reed to the mouthpiece using the ligature. The end of the reed needs to be *exactly* level with and central to the tip of the mouthpiece. This can be a fiddly operation at first.

5. The clarinet is supported by the right thumb, which is placed under the thumb rest at the back of the instrument. It might take a while to get used to this, but it is important to adopt a good posture.

Gently push the mouthpiece onto the barrel. This might require a light twisting action, and in any case make sure the cork is greased.

Spread a little grease on the cork from time to time to prevent cracking.

CORK GREASE

Important
Always use the pull-through to dry your clarinet after playing.

Lesson 1

goals:

1. **Breathing using the diaphragm**
2. **Posture and hand positioning**
3. **Formation of the mouth shape (embouchure)**
4. **Tonguing**
5. **The notes E, D and C**
6. **Counting while playing; semibreves, minims and crotchets**

Breathing

A relaxed, controlled posture is essential for comfort and correct breathing.

When breathing in and out, always use your diaphragm. This is a large membrane underneath your rib cage which causes your stomach to go *out* when breathing in and to go *in* when breathing out.

You will be able to control your breathing far more effectively using your diaphragm than if you were to breathe with the *intercostal* muscles high up in your chest.

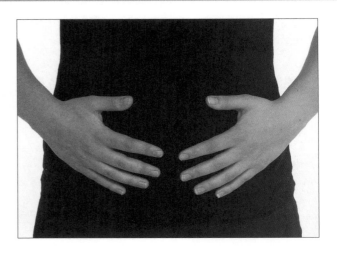

Exercise 1:

Breathe in counting four beats, then breathe out counting 4 and so on, always using the diaphragm and maintaining a steady flow of air.

In, 2, 3, 4,   Out, 2, 3, 4,   In...

Place one hand on your belly to check whether it is going out as you breathe in then in when you breathe out.

Posture and holding the clarinet

Stand in a relaxed, upright way, feet slightly apart.

Place the joint of your right thumb underneath the thumb rest halfway down the clarinet.

Now cover the thumb hole with your left thumb.

The fingers of each hand should curl around the body of the clarinet to the front, making sure they do not push against any keys at the sides.

The clarinet is held at an angle such that your right thumb should be about fifteen centimetres away from your body.

Embouchure

Turn your bottom lip in slightly so that it rests on your bottom teeth.

Place the mouthpiece in your mouth so that the reed lies on the centre of your bottom lip with about a centimetre of the reed inside your mouth.

Rest your top teeth on the top of the mouthpiece, and, while smiling slightly and keeping a pointed chin, close the sides of your mouth around the mouthpiece

The lips should form a firm, airtight seal around the mouthpiece. Make sure the cheeks remain taught: don't puff them out.

Exercise 2:

Set your top teeth and bottom lip on the mouthpiece. Breathe in through the corners of your mouth over the count of 4, close the mouth and breathe out attempting to produce a note. Don't puff out your cheeks.

Breathe,   play,

- If you are able to play a note, well done – you are on your way!
- If you just hear the sound of air blowing down the clarinet, tighten your embouchure around the mouthpiece a bit, but don't bite.
- If the airway is blocked when you try to play, this is because you are closing the gap between the reed and the mouthpiece. Loosen your embouchure a bit.
- If you make a nasty squeak, it is probably because your bottom teeth are touching the reed. Remember it is the bottom lip that must support the reed.

Tonguing

Say the word **Dee** several times. The tongue acts as a valve that blocks the air until the precise moment that the word is started. Notes on the clarinet should be started in this way to ensure a clean *attack*.

Breathe in and form the correct embouchure as described above. Place your tongue along the underside of the reed so there is about a half a centimetre of contact, from the tip of the tongue to the tip of the reed.

Start a note by releasing the tongue from the reed as in the word **Dee**.
The note should have a definite and tidy beginning.

Exercise 3:

Play the following notes in time, ensuring you tongue each one.

Breathe,   tongue,

Lesson 1

The notes E, D and C

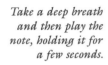

Take a deep breath and then play the note, holding it for a few seconds.

T = *Thumb hole*

 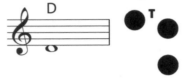 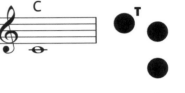

E

D

C

T

left hand

L1
L2
L3

right hand

R1
R2
R3

> **NOTE**
> The fingering diagrams throughout this book are shown as if viewed from the front

---

Exercise 4:

Breathe before the beginning of this exercise and in the rests.

Don't forget to tongue each note. A four beat note is called a **semibreve**.

Exercise 5:

Each of the notes and rests here are **minims** worth two beats.

Exercise 6:

These notes and rests are all **crotchets** worth one beat each.

Breathe in quickly during crotchet rests.

Pieces for Lesson 1

Valley Song

Going Cuckoo

Au Clair de la Lune

Lesson 2 goals:

1. The note F
2. Open throat breathing
3. Dotted minims
4. Three beats in a bar

The note F

F

OPENING YOUR THROAT

Blow on the back of your hand. You will feel the air is cold. Now try again, pretending that you are steaming up a window. This time the air on the back of your hand should feel warm because you have just breathed out with your throat open. You should keep your throat open at all times when playing as it will improve your tone.

Exercise 1:

Stand with a relaxed posture, take a good deep breath and play the note with an open throat, using the diaphragm to control the air flow.

The symbol above this note is called a **pause** (or *fermata*). It means you should hold the note on for longer than its actual value of four beats. Hold this one on for as long as you can. Play with an **open throat**.

Long notes like this one should be the first thing you practise every day.

Exercise 2:

Play these notes in tempo with an open throat. The little commas are *breath* marks.

Take a very quick breath here without disrupting the 4 beat count.

Exercise 3:

Keep your first finger close to the E key when you take it off to play F. (Don't point forwards.)

This will allow you to play quicker and to be more precise when replacing it after each F.

Don't be satisfied with any untidiness!

Dotted notes

A dot placed to the right of a note multiplies its duration (value) by one and a half.

This means that a minim with a dot would increase in duration from two beats to three (2+1=3).

Count: 1   2   3   4   1   2   3   4

Exercise 4:

Count carefully as you play these notes. Remember the open throat.

Time Signatures

So far all the exercises and pieces have had a **time signature** of four beats to every bar:

1, 2, 3, 4, **1**, 2, 3, 4, **1**, 2, 3, 4 etc.

Many pieces, however, contain three beats per bar.

This means that the count in your head will be **1**, 2, 3, **1**, 2, 3, **1**, 2, 3 etc.

A waltz is a dance that uses this time signature.

Exercise 5:

Count three beats per bar, as shown by the top number of the time signature, and make sure you don't get confused between notes in spaces (F and D) and notes on lines (E and C).

Count: 1   2   3   1   2   3   1   2   3

THINK!

Are you still relaxed when you play? Remember to keep your shoulders down and breathe using your diaphragm.

Are the corners of your mouth still smiling and is your chin still pointed?

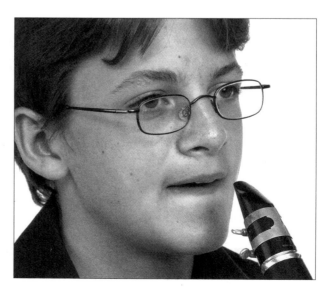

Check the lip: the support for the reed needs to be in the lip, not the bottom teeth.

Pieces for Lesson 2

Back To Bed

Grumpy Graham

Medieval Dance

Barcarolle

Offenbach

goals:

1. **The note G**
2. **Tied notes**

The note G

Although no fingers are needed to cover any keys or holes for this note, care must be taken to ensure you are in control of the clarinet.

Keep a good support with your right thumb under the thumb rest and don't move your fingers far from the keys or holes.

G

Exercise 1:

Play this one a few times, holding the note for as long as is comfortable.

Exercise 2:

Remember to tongue the beginning of each note.

Exercise 3:

Play this one many times to ensure that your tongue, fingers and thumb (if needed) all move together.

Exercise 4:

Don't get confused between C, E and G which all look a bit similar.

Lesson 3

Ties and tied notes

Two notes of the same pitch can be joined together to make a longer note by *tying* them together. A curved line is drawn from one to the other to show this. The note is then held on for the *combined value* of the two notes. This is usually needed if a note needs to carry on into the next bar.

Here are some examples.

Is held for **3** beats   Is held for **6** beats

Exercise 5:

Count very carefully here.

Count: 1   2   3   4   1   2...

✳ **The following piece does not appear in the saxophone book**

Exercise 6: off beats

Try to keep your counting relaxed while playing these off beats

Student

Teacher

THINK!

Are you playing with *warm air* because your throat is open?

Are you keeping your fingers close to the body of the clarinet?

Pieces for Lesson 3

Jingle Bells

Largo (from the New World Symphony)

Dvořák

Lightly Row

Knight Time

1. **The note A**
2. **Dynamics (loud and soft)**
3. **Slurred notes**

The note A

A is played by *rotating* your index finger upwards so the side of the finger opens the key. This will ensure smoothness when approaching A from lower notes.

Exercise 1:

Rolling the index finger.

Dynamics

Notes and rhythms are two of the elements of music, but without expression, music can be lifeless and mechanical. One of the obvious ways of introducing *colour* into music is to play sections of pieces or phrases at different levels of loudness.

f stands for the word *forte* and means loud.   *p* stands for the word *piano* which means quiet.

Exercise 2:

It's often harder to play a piece slowly and accurately than to bluff your way through it quickly.

Take your time and aim for a clear, confident style.

Play these notes according to the dynamic displayed underneath.

Use your diaphragm to increase the air flow for the loud notes, and decrease the air flow for the quiet ones.

Exercise 3:

This is a note-twister. Always **roll** your index finger to the A key without lifting it.

Play this slowly at first, then try to build up speed each time you practise it. Can you play it in one breath?

Exercise 4:

These notes are all written on spaces. Don't get D, F and A confused.

Slurs

In all the pieces and exercises so far you have tongued every note, that is: you have started each note with a **D** as in **dee**. This can make the music sound a bit disjointed, and spoils the flow of gentle pieces such as *Barcarolle* in Lesson 2.

Music is made smoother by slurring notes together. This means you should only tongue the note where the slur begins. All other notes included in the slur are played by just changing the fingering.

Slurs are shown by lines which look like ties, but the notes will be of different pitches.

Be sure to give a clean, crisp end to your notes by bringing your tongue back onto the reed rather than by just stopping breathing, especially at the end of a piece or at a rest.

Exercise 5: slurred pairs

Only tongue the first of each pair of notes, but keep the air flowing as you play the second.

Exercise 6:

Here you need to slur three notes at a time. The steady **1**, 2, 3 count is unaffected by slurs.

Exercise 7:

Try *Barcarolle* again with slurs and with the dynamic shown. It should sound much more like a lullaby.

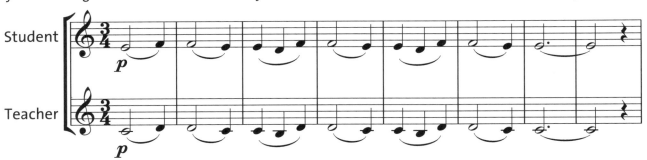

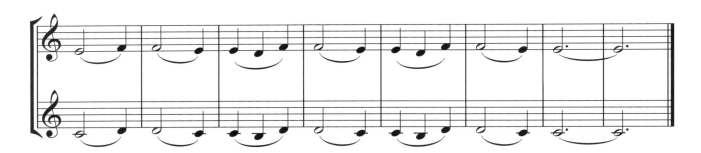

Pieces for Lesson 4

 19 – 20

When The Saints Go Marching In

 21 – 22

Joshua Fought The Battle Of Jericho

Spiritual

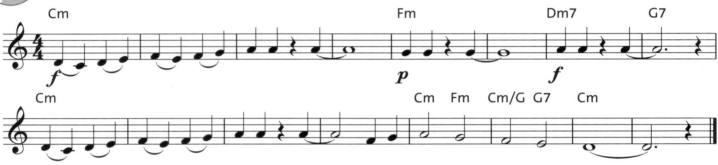

23 – 24

Coventry Carol (adapted)

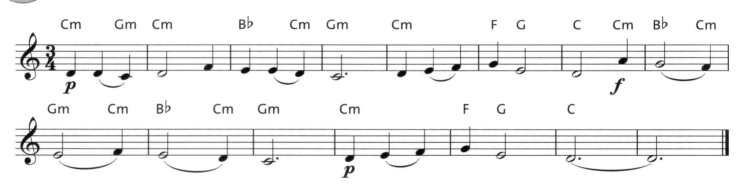

Canon For Two

The second player begins one bar behind the first player.

goals:

1. **The note F sharp (F#)**
2. **Tones and Semitones**
3. **Repeat signs**

The note F#

Keep your unused fingers curled round the clarinet and your right thumb close to the thumb hole.

Compare this note with F and G. You will hear that F# is half way between.

The difference in pitch between F and G is called a **tone**.
F to F# is only a **semitone**.
F# to G is also a **semitone**.

A semitone is the smallest *interval* that can be played on most instruments.

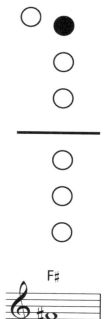

Exercise 1:

Use your right thumb to support the clarinet.

Exercise 2:

Compare F to G (a tone) with F to F# (a semitone). The *natural* sign is to remind you when to play a normal F. Move your hand as little as possible.
The thick bar-lines with two dots tell you to **repeat** the music between them, in other words play twice.

repeat sign

Exercise 3: sharps and naturals

All the Fs here are natural unless: they have a sharp symbol immediately before them; they come after an F# in the same bar and don't have a natural sign.

Pieces for Lesson 5

Jingle Bells

Abide With Me

Monk

Juggling

test: *for* Lessons 1 to 5

1. Note duration

On the stave below, draw notes of the indicated duration:

(4)

2. Rests

On the stave below, draw rests of the indicated duration:

(4)

3. Notes

On the stave below, draw the following notes as minims:

C, E, A, F, D and **F♯**

(8)

4. Sharp thinking

How many **F♯**s do you play in this piece? _____

(2)

5. Bars

Draw bar lines on this stave where they are needed.

(7)

Total **(25)**

Lesson 6 goals:

1. The note B
2. Key signatures and their meaning
3. The keys of C, F and G majors

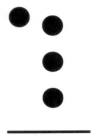

The note B

This note is a semitone below C.

Exercise 1:

Listen to how close B and C sound

Exercise 2: wide leaps

Keep all hand and finger movements tidy, and remember to roll your finger to the A key in the 2nd bar.

Different Keys

If you try to sing a simple tune such as *The Star Spangled Banner*, you may find early on that you can't reach the high notes without really straining. The solution is to start the piece a little lower. This time, you may be able to sing the high notes perfectly. You are now singing the piece in a different **key**.

There are many different keys in music, each of which needs its own set of notes. The key of **C major** is easy as it requires no sharps. The key of **G major** requires all **F**s to be played as **F♯**. The key of **F** requires all **B**s to be played as **B♭** (see lesson 9). These necessary alterations will be shown as the **key signature** at the beginning of every line of music.

C major

G major

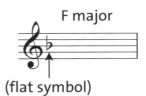
F major

(flat symbol)

Exercise 3: comparison

Play the opening to this well known carol first in the key of F major, then in the key of G major.
Notice that the key signature tells you that all Fs are in fact F♯s otherwise the tune will sound wrong.

F major

G major

Pieces for Lesson 6

Barcarolle

(learn the bottom part this time!)

Offenbach

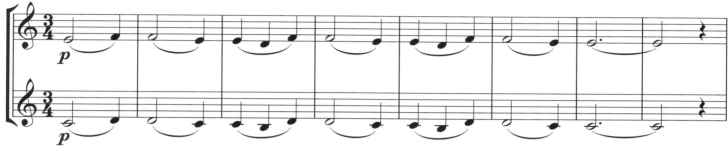

In Paris

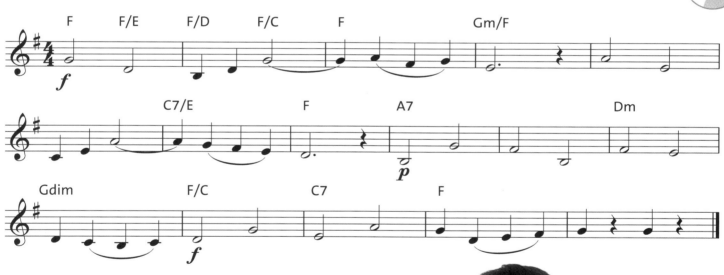

THINK!

Do you start every practice session with long notes?
They are the best way to improve your tone and build up your strength.

Pieces for Lesson 6

When The Saints Go Marching In

(The key of this piece is D major, but don't worry about the C♯ in the key signature.
You won't need to play a C♯).

Steal Away

Spiritual

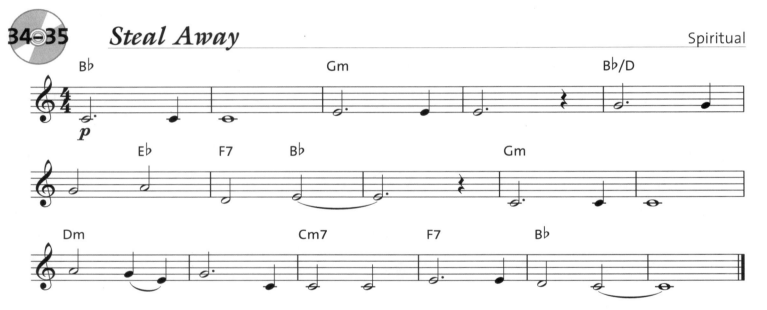

From *The Unfinished Symphony*

Schubert

Count up to 6 in each bar for this one, and watch out for the F♯s!
Although the key is F major, you won't need to play any B♭s here.

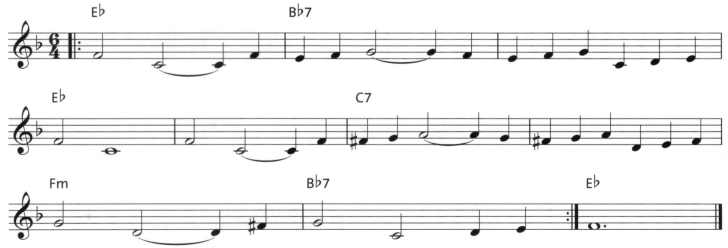

Pieces for Lesson 6

Nkosi Sikelel'

E. Mankayi Sontonga

Magnetic Forks

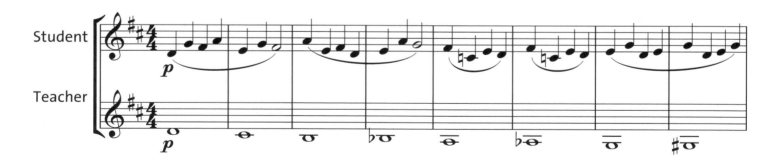

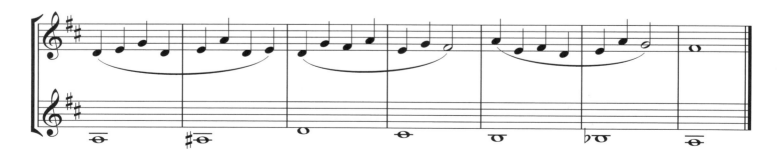

Lesson 7 goals:

1. **The notes A and G**
2. **Octaves**
3. **Common time**

The notes A and G

A

G

Octaves

Practice makes perfect. Perseverance will be rewarded with a good, strong tone.

Make sure you are breathing from your diaphragm for complete breath control, and experiment with your embouchure. And most important of all: relax!

You have already seen how to play the notes A and G in lessons 3 and 4. However, the new notes for this sound the same but rather lower.

Exercise 1:

Compare the sounds of low A with the *higher* A and low G with the *higher* G.

The large **C** at the beginning of this stave is short-hand for **Common Time** which is the same as $\frac{4}{4}$

Exercise 2:

Low notes can be very satisfying to play as long as your throat is open. Imagine trying to steam up the inside of the clarinet with your breath.

Pieces for Lesson 7

O Come All Ye Faithful

Skye Boat Song

Scottish traditional

Repeat the section within the repeat signs, then go back to the beginning and play until
the sign *Fine* (Italian for end).

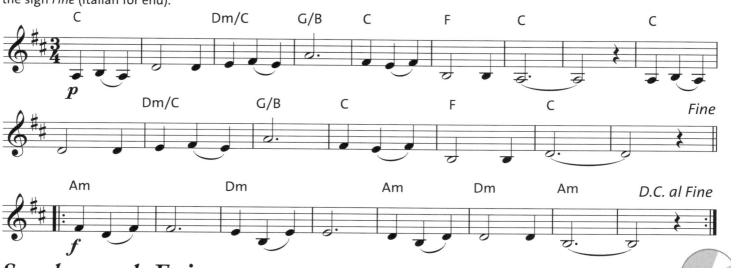

Scarborough Fair

English traditional

You could play the top part or the bottom part. If you feel ambitious, learn both!

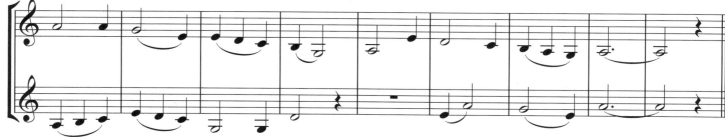

goals:

1. **Quavers**
2. **G major scale**
3. **Tempo and character markings**

Quavers

Sight-reading (playing music that you haven't seen before) is an important skill for a musician.

Get into the habit of finding music you haven't played before and trying to play it straight off. You'll be surprised how much easier this becomes once you get used to it.

Remember to keep a steady beat and the rhythm will take care of itself.

So far you have studied and played notes that last for four beats (semibreve), two beats (minim), and one beat (crotchet). You have also learnt how to increase note durations by tying notes together or by adding a dot to a minim (for a three beat note).

Quavers are notes which last for *half* the length of a crotchet and should therefore be played *twice* as fast.

Single quavers and a quaver rest

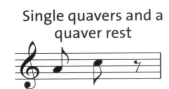

Quavers in pairs (worth 1 crotchet per pair)

Quavers as a group (a minim's worth)

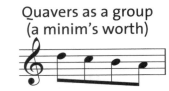

Exercise 1: *double or quit!*

Keep the beat steady and don't start too quickly.

Count: 1 2 3 4   1 2 3 4   1 2 3 4   1 & 2 & 3 & 4 &   1 2 3 4

Exercise 2: three beats per bar

Count: 1   2   3   1   2   3   1 & 2 & 3 &   1   2   3

Exercise 3: the scale of G major

Play your scales steadily and slowly – try to make the notes sound as though they belong together.

A scale is a series of notes that move up or down by step from one note to the same note an octave higher or lower. Play this both slurred and tongued (as shown by the dotted slur lines).

Pieces for Lesson 8

Some short melodies for practice at playing quavers.

Yankee Doodle

This piece has only two beats per bar, and notice the tempo (speed) marking above the beginning of the piece.

Can Can

Offenbach

Nessun Dorma

Puccini

From *The Magic Flute*

Mozart

Swing Low, Sweet Chariot

Spiritual

Lesson 9 goals:

1. **The notes low and high B♭**
2. **Dotted crotchets**
3. **Anacrusis (up beat)**

The notes low and high B♭

B♭

The ♭ symbol lowers the note to which it applies by a semitone.

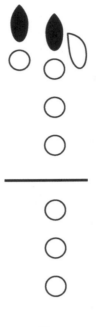

B♭

B♭ is a semitone below B and a semitone above A.

Exercise 1:

Roll both your index finger and your thumb upwards for the high B♭.

Play each note for as long as you can. Every time you practice you should start with long notes!

Dotted crotchets

Dotted notes are often used instead of tying notes together: the fewer symbols there are on the page, the easier the music is to read.

As long ago as lesson 2 you discovered that a dot placed to the right of a minim increased its value from two beats to three. You could say that the dot *multiplies* its length by one and a half.

The same **dot** can be used to increase a crotchet's length from one beat to one and a half beats. In other words, instead of being the same length as two quavers tied together, its value is raised to three quavers.

Exercise 2:

Play this slowly so that you can count each quaver. Learn to recognise the rhythms as you recognise words without really having to read them.

Count: 1 & 2 & 3 & 4 & 1 & 2 & 3 & 4 & 1 etc.

Exercise 3:

Play this exercise a few times increasing the speed a little each time. In time you should feel the rhythm by recognising the pattern of notes and rely less on having to count each quaver.

Exercise 4:

Because this type of rhythm is very common but a little tricky, here is another exercise.
This time there are three beats to a bar.

Anacrusis

Sometimes a piece of music doesn't begin with a whole bar.

The next piece begins with a single beat representing the last beat of a bar. This short bar (called an up beat or *anacrusis*) is balanced by another short bar at the end. The two short bars add up to a whole bar.

Pieces for Lesson 9

Auld Lang Syne

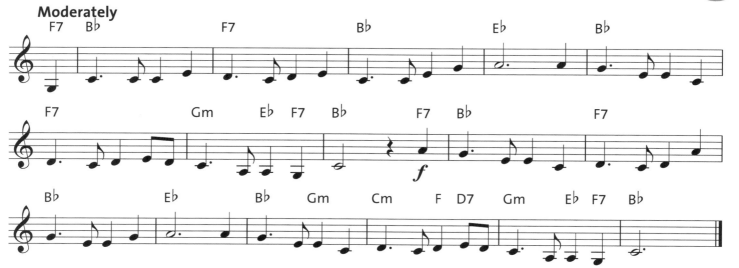

Pieces for Lesson 9

57

Allegro from *Spring* (adapted)

Vivaldi

Allegro is the Italian word for quick and is very commonly seen as a tempo marking in music.

The top line here is the main tune, but you could also learn the bottom line for duet playing.

THINK!

Are you practising properly?
Always start with long notes, making sure you are using your diaphragm and open throat. Stay relaxed when you play. Practise your exercises every day to improve your tone and dexterity. Don't be satisfied if a piece is nearly right.
It needs to be completely right before you should move on.

goals:

1. The note low F
2. More dynamics

Lesson
10

The note low F

As with the other low notes (A and G) you must ensure that you play this note with an open throat for a warm and pleasing tone.

Exercise 1:

Play these long notes with an open throat and controlled breath.

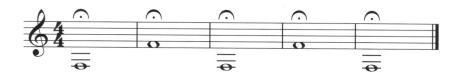

Exercise 2:

Here is a *scale* of F major. Practise this first with every note tongued, then with all slurred. You will need to take a big breath.

More dynamics

Only p and f have been introduced so far. These tell you to play either quietly or loudly, however, in between these extremes you could play *moderately quiet* or *moderately loud* These are shown by the markings mp and mf. The m is short for *mezzo* which is the Italian word for half.

Exercise 3:

Play these notes with the dynamics indicated.

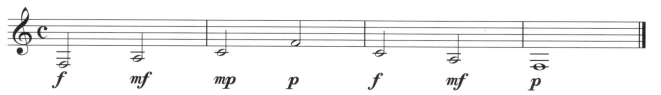

Try to make sure that the first forte *is exactly as loud as the second* forte: *it's easy to lose track of just how loud you are, especially when the dynamics vary so much.*

Watch out that your mp *isn't too quiet, otherwise you won't be able to come down further for the* p.

35

Pieces for Lesson 10

58-59 *Silent Night*

Grüber

Watch out for the low F at the end and observe the dynamics.

60-61 *Dixie*

Emmett

Moderately quick

62 From *Symphony No.9* (play either part)

Beethoven

test: *for* Lessons 6 to 10

1. Note duration

On the stave below, draw notes of the indicated duration:

I quaver   2 beats-worth of quavers   dotted crotchet   a note that lasts for 5 quavers

(8)

2. Scale

On the stave below, draw the G major scale including the correct key signature:

(4)

3. Notes

On the stave below draw the following notes as crotchets:

F, low F, high A, B, low G, high B♭, E, F♯

(4)

4. Dynamics

What are the Italian words for:

Moderately loud _____

Moderately quiet _____

(4)

5. Naming ceremony

Identify all the items indicated by arrows.

(5)

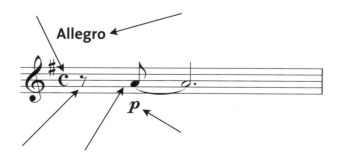

Allegro

p

Total **(25)**

37

Lesson 11

goals:

1. The note E flat (E♭)
2. The key of B♭ major

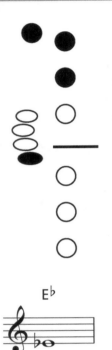

E♭

The note E♭

As seen in lesson 9, the **flat** symbol *lowers* the note to which it applies by one semitone. This means that E♭ is a semitone below E, and a semitone above D.

Exercise 1:

As with playing all notes on the clarinet, make sure your fingers and hands move swiftly and with the minimum of movement necessary.

Exercise 2:

The key signature of B♭ major is B♭ and E♭. Practise this scale both tongued and slurred.

Flat signs are shown in brackets to remind you to play E♭s.

However, it is important to observe the key signature and automatically play sharpened or flattened notes according to the key specified.

Exercise 3:

Flat out concentration.

Notes are marked E♮ or E♭. Make sure your fingers respond accordingly.

Pieces for Lesson 11

Frère Jacques

French traditional

Up to four people can play this as a round. Begin when the previous instrument reaches the star in the 3rd bar.

Romance No.1

Beethoven

63–64

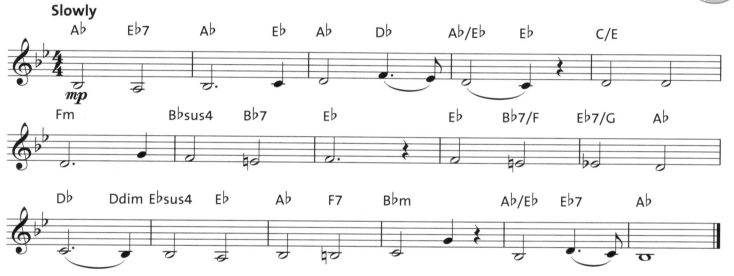

Can Can

Offenbach

65–66

Compare this version in B♭ major with the one in G major in lesson 8.

Lesson 12

goals:
1. **The register key**
2. **The notes C,D,E, F and G with the register key**
3. **DS al Fine**

You might find that these high notes sound a little out of tune when you first play them.

Keep a firm embouchure to ensure a steady tone and correct tuning.

The notes C,D,E, F and G with the register key

You have already used the register key for the note B♭, however its main use is for playing notes in the *upper register*. You will find that any note played with the register key will sound a twelfth (an octave and a fifth) higher than the note played without it.

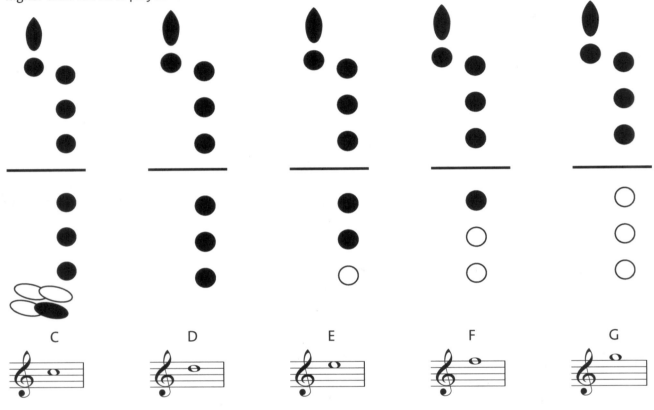

Exercise 1:

Just roll your thumb up to touch the register key (while still covering the thumb hole) to change from each low note to the higher one.

Exercise 2: octave leaps

Play this very slowly at first to get used to the different fingerings between the low and high notes.

Exercise 3:

Recognising higher notes.

Pieces for Lesson 12

When The Saints Go Marching In

Play the section between the repeat bars twice. The first time, play the two bars at the end labelled 1, the second time play the bars labelled 2. These are called *first and second time bars*.

Reveille

Military traditional

DS al Fine means go back to the sign (𝄋) and play again until *Fine* (end.)

The note B (left fingering) with the register key

The break

One of the hardest aspects of clarinet playing is crossing from one register to another.

This is called playing *over the break*. You will need to practice patiently to achieve smoothness.

Exercise 1:

Keep your right hand fingers on keys.

Exercise 2:

Practice will help to build up 'muscle memory': eventually you won't have to think about which fingers are required for a particular note, as your hands will 'know' what to do.

Apart from the D which needs only 3 fingers, keep all 4 fingers of your right hand down.

Exercise 3:

Keep all your right hand fingers down (including the fourth finger).

Exercise 4:

Work out for yourself which fingers you can keep down here.

Exercise 5: scales of C major and F major

With practice the break should be undetectable to a listener.

Pieces for Lesson 13

Camptown Races

Foster

When can you keep your right hand fingers down?

Home On The Range

Here's a piece to test your smooth playing over the break

Pieces for Lesson 13

71-72 ***Danny Boy***   Irish traditional

This is one of the most beautiful tunes ever written. Spend time on this to ensure complete fluency,
control of dynamics and the correct slurs – it will be time well spent.

73 ***Swing Low, Sweet Chariot***   Spiritual

goals:

1. **The note C sharp (C♯)**
2. **Alternative fingerings for B and C♯**
3. **Minor keys and scales**

The note C♯

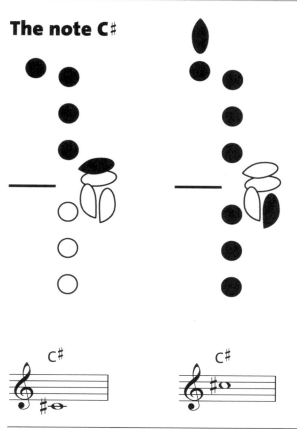

B (right fingering)

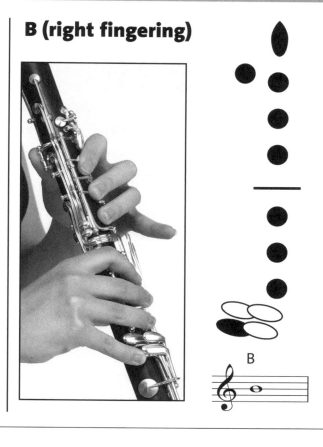

Certain notes can be played in more than one way. The B fingering here should be used when it comes before C♯.

See exercises 3 and 4 for more details, and take a look at the pull-out fingering chart for a complete list of alternative fingerings.

Exercise 1: low C, C♯ and D

Get used to the fingering as soon as you can.

Exercise 2:

Moving up and down by semitones. Do this slowly until your fingers are confident.

 *The following two pieces do **not** appear in the saxophone book*

Alternative fingerings

There are several notes on the clarinet that have more than one possible fingering.

This is because certain changes would be awkward otherwise: try this:

B to C is easy, but B to C♯ would require a magic little finger!

The alternative B fingering to solve this problem is shown at the top of the page.

Exercise 3:

Follow the L / R guides to show you which fingering to use.

right hand fingers down

Major and minor

Some people think of major keys as being bright, whilst minor keys are dark.

The mood created has to do with the sequence of intervals that makes up the scale for the key.

Most of the pieces you have played up to now have sounded cheerful. That is because they are virtually all in a *major* key, C major, F major, G major and so on. Sometimes, however, a composer wishes to express sadness in a piece. In general he will do this by writing the piece in a *minor* key.

Exercise 4: the D major scale

Play this a few times and listen to its bright character. You could try B with the right-hand little finger, and C# with the left-hand little finger! Just make sure that you change hands from one note to the other.

Exercise 5: D minor

The *key signature* (B♭) is the same as F major, however look out for the C#s which are shown as they occur in the music. (These are called **accidentals**.)

Pieces for Lesson 14

74-75

Hava Nagila

Israeli traditional

A famous tune in a minor key (Gm). Start slowly and get faster as you go along. This should sound exciting!

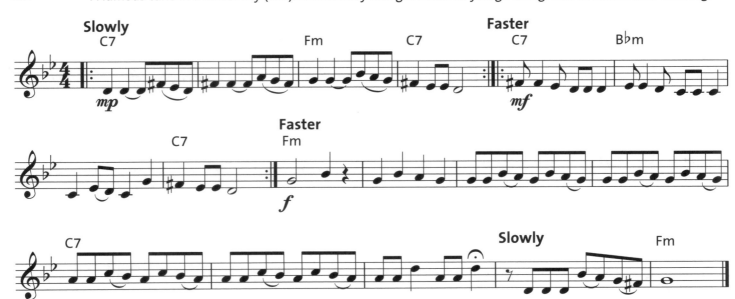

46

Pieces for Lesson 14

Go Down Moses

Spiritual

The melody is divided up amongst the three clarinets so they are all equally important.

Use the written dynamics to blend in when you are playing an accompanying line.

Slowly

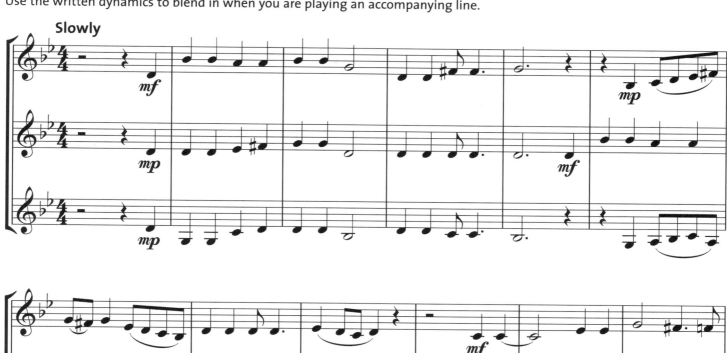

Lesson 15 goals:

1. **The notes F♯ and A with the register key**
2. **Staccato and legato**

The note F♯

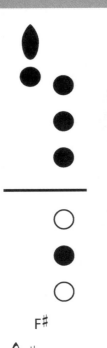

F♯

A + register key

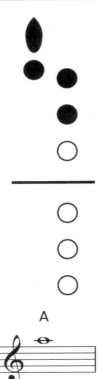

A

Exercise 1:
Remember diaphragm support, and an open throat.

High notes only use a very short length of the instrument to make a sound. For this reason they need less breath for the same volume than a low note.

Exercise 2:
This is an A minor arpeggio extending over 2 octaves.

Be careful not to use too much breath on high notes, otherwise it may affect the tone and the tuning — and your ears!

Exercise 3: low and high
Play slowly to ensure a warm and even tone for all notes.

Staccato and legato

Legato means joined up and refers to notes that are slurred or tongued smoothly without a gap from the previous one. *Staccato* on the other hand means detached. This is shown by a dot above or below the note.

Exercise 4:

Repeat this many times to achieve clear staccato tonguing.

Exercise 5:

Begin this very slowly otherwise the quavers will be too fast to tongue.

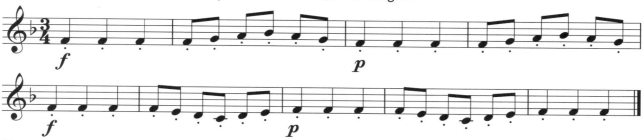

 The following exercise does not appear in the saxophone book

Exercise 6: staccato and legato

Pieces for Lesson 15

The Blue Danube Waltz

Johann Strauss II

Pieces for Lesson 15

78-79 *Oh! Susannah*

Stephen Foster

Moderately

80-81 **Song Of The Volga Boatmen**

Russian traditional

Gravely

82-83 *Mango Walk*

Jamaican traditional

Moderately

50

1. Key signatures

On the stave below, draw the correct key signatures for:

G major   F major   D minor   D major   C major

(5)

2. Dots

Simplify the music on the left using dots to get rid of the ties.

(5)

3. Notes

On the stave below draw the following notes as crotchets:

C ♯, low F, top G, E ♭, B, high A

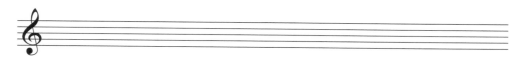

(6)

4. Dynamics

What do the following words mean?

legato _____

staccato _____

(4)

5. Naming ceremony

Identify all the items indicated by arrows.

(5)

Total **(25)**

Lesson 16

goals:

1. **The notes A flat (A♭) and E♭ with the register key**
2. **Enharmonic notes**

The notes A♭ and E♭ with the register key

Compare the two A♭ notes an octave apart. Try to keep the tone as similar as possible despite the big difference in pitch. Both notes should sound as though they are coming from the same instrument.

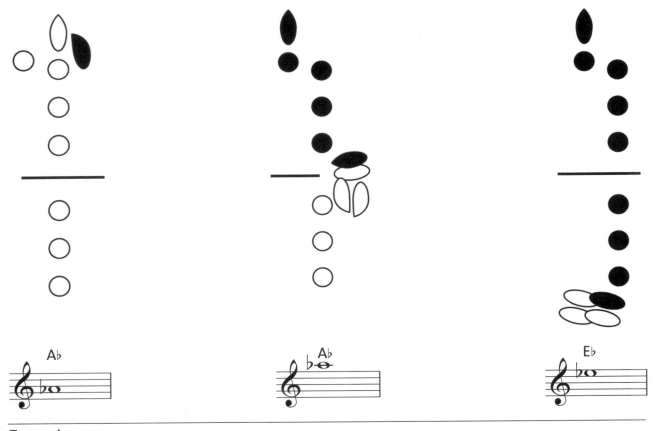

Exercise 1:

Play these long notes. Use a full breath for each one.

Enharmonic notes

From previous lessons, you will know that A♭ is a semitone *below* A, and at the same time a semitone *above* G. This means that the same note could be called G♯. These two notes are *enharmonic equivalents*.

Exercise 2:

These two short pieces need a note you have just learnt, the first as a G♯, the second as an A♭.

Exercise 3:

Play the following notes. You *do* know the fingering for each one, however you may need to write down their enharmonic equivalents first.

Pieces for Lesson 16

The Entertainer

Scott Joplin

84

Not fast

Enharmonic Blues

85-86

Slow blues tempo

Lesson 17 goals:

1. **Gradation of dynamics**
2. **More Italian terms**

Dynamic markings and tempo markings are very useful.

Music should always be expressive, and these markings will give a clue to the way a piece should be played.

All dynamic changes you have played so far have been instant. However, suddenly changing from *piano* to *forte* has a different impact from a gradual change.

Crescendo means gradually get louder, also shown as:

Diminuendo means gradually get quieter, also shown as:

Some other commonly used Italian words to describe a tempo are:

Allegro quickly   **Andante** at a walking pace   **Adagio** slowly

Rallentando (rall.) becoming slower   **Accelerando** (accel.) becoming faster

Pieces for Lesson 17

87   *La Forza del Destino*

Verdi

54

Hail The Conquering Hero (from *Judas Maccabeus*)

Handel

88

William Tell Overture

Rossini

89

goals:

1. **Swing quavers**
2. **Playing jazz pieces**

Swing

Remember not to play the quavers too 'straight', but instead give them a healthy bounce.

You might imagine the beat divided into three, with the first two-thirds for the first quaver and the final third for the second quaver.

In classical music all quavers are played exactly as written: that is, lasting half as long as a crotchet.

In jazz, however, quavers are normally played unevenly, with the first of each pair longer than half a beat, and the second shorter to compensate. This is called **swing**.

Exercise 1:

Play this A minor scale in swing rhythm. Try it first all tongued, then with the slurs as written.

Pieces for Lesson 18

90–91 *Little Brown Jug*

92–93 *Joshua Jazz*

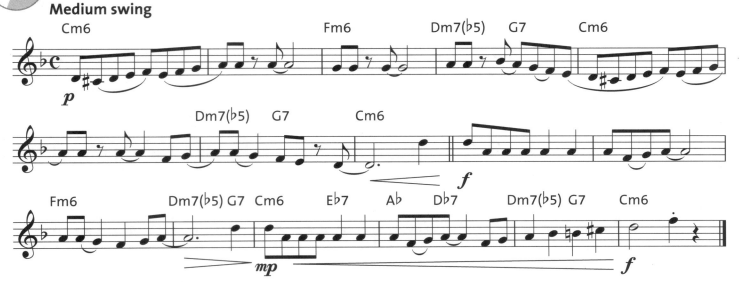

Pieces for Lesson 18

Maryland, My Maryland

goals:

1. **Good technique through scale practice**
2. **Ensemble playing**

Practising

Practising scales every day will help you to:

* Train your fingers to respond quickly in various keys
* Ensure evenness in the timing of notes
* Develop a consistent tone over the instrument's range
* Increase control over your breathing
* Improve your listening awareness of note relationships

The following scales and arpeggios are recommended practice for clarinettists at a relatively early stage. They should be practised both slurred and tongued.

F major

G major

C major

D minor

A minor

Pieces for Lesson 19

Gypsy Rover

 Lesson 19

Pieces for Lesson 19

Down By The Riverside

Lively swing

goals:

Lesson 20

1. 6/8 time signature (compound time)
2. Traditional-style songs in 6/8 time

Simple and compound time

$\frac{2}{4}$, $\frac{3}{4}$, and $\frac{4}{4}$ are all *simple* time signatures.

The top number tells you how many beats per bar, and the bottom number tells you that each beat is worth one crotchet. This also means that each beat can be divided into **two** quavers.

Exercise 1: counting in simple time

Count: 1   2   3   4   1 & 2 & 3 & 4 &   1...

In *compound* time, however, each beat is worth **three** quavers.

This means that each beat must now be a *dotted* crotchet.

Exercise 2: counting in compound time

Count: 1 & a 2 & a 1 & a 2 & a 1   2

Exercise 3:

Here's a well-known tune in $\frac{6}{8}$ time. Remember to think in *two*.

Count: 1 & a 2 & a 1 & a 2 & a 1 & a 2 & a 1...

Irish jigs are in 6/8 time, as is the well-known 'We're Off To See The Wizard' from The Wizard Of Oz. 6/8 pieces are often lively. Counting two lots of three is much easier than trying to count all six quavers.

THINK!

Remember to keep a steady beat. You might want to use a metronome. Some people like to tap their foot when they play, but this takes a little practice before it comes naturally.

61

Pieces for Lesson 20

95

The Animals Went In Two By Two

Traditional

96-97

For He's A Jolly Good Fellow

Traditional

test: *for* Lessons 16 to 20

1. Enharmonic

Rewrite the following notes as their enharmonic equivalents:

(5)

2. Afraid of heights?

Write the following music one octave higher.

(6)

3. Breath control

Play this note with a steady tone, controlling your breath at all times.

You will score one mark (up to a maximum of five) for every three seconds held.

(5)

4. Expression

Write the Italian words for:

Get louder _____   Get quieter _____

Get quicker _____   Get slower _____

(4)

5. Scale test

Play the following from memory:

1. **D minor scale**

2. **C major arpeggio**

3. **F major scale**

(5)

4. **G major arpeggio**

5. **A minor scale**

Total (25)

CD backing tracks

1 Tuning track
2 Virtuoso Performance
3 Valley Song
4 Going Cuckoo
5 Au Clair de la Lune *demonstration*
6 Au Clair de la Lune *backing only*
7 Back To Bed *demonstration*
8 Back To Bed *backing only*
9 Grumpy Graham
10 Medieval Dance
11 Barcarolle
12 Jingle Bells *demonstration*
13 Jingle Bells *backing only*
14 Largo from New World Symphony *demonstration*
15 Largo from New World Symphony *backing only*
16 Lightly Row
17 Knight Time *demonstration*
18 Knight Time *backing only*
19 When The Saints Go Marching In *demonstration*
20 When The Saints Go Marching In *backing only*
21 Joshua Fought The Battle Of Jericho *demonstration*
22 Joshua Fought The Battle Of Jericho *backing only*
23 Coventry Carol *demonstration*
24 Coventry Carol *backing only*
25 Jingle Bells *demonstration*
26 Jingle Bells *backing only*
27 Abide With Me
28 Juggling *demonstration*
29 Juggling *backing only*
30 In Paris *demonstration*
31 In Paris *backing only*
32 When The Saints Go Marching In *demonstration*
33 When The Saints Go Marching In *backing only*
34 Steal Away *demonstration*
35 Steal Away *backing only*

36 The Unfinished Symphony *demonstration*
37 The Unfinished Symphony *backing only*
38 Nkosi Sikelel'
39 Magnetic Forks
40 O Come All Ye Faithful *demonstration*
41 O Come All Ye Faithful *backing only*
42 Skye Boat Song *demonstration*
43 Skye Boat Song *backing only*
44 Scarborough Fair
45 Yankee Doodle *demonstration*
46 Yankee Doodle *backing only*
47 Can Can *demonstration*
48 Can Can *backing only*
49 Nessun Dorma *demonstration*
50 Nessun Dorma *backing only*
51 Magic Flute *demonstration*
52 Magic Flute *backing only*
53 Swing Low, Sweet Chariot *demonstration*
54 Swing Low, Sweet Chariot *backing only*
55 Auld Lang Syne *demonstration*
56 Auld Lang Syne *backing only*
57 Allegro from Spring
58 Silent Night *demonstration*
59 Silent Night *backing only*
60 Dixie *demonstration*
61 Dixie *backing only*
62 from Symphony No. 9
63 Romance No.1 *demonstration*
64 Romance No.1 *backing only*
65 Can Can *demonstration*
66 Can Can *backing only*
67 When The Saints Go Marching In
68 Camptown Races
69 Home On The Range *demonstration*
70 Home On The Range *backing only*
71 Danny Boy *demonstration*
72 Danny Boy *backing only*

73 Swing Low, Sweet Chariot
74 Hava Nagila *demonstration*
75 Hava Nagila *backing only*
76 The Blue Danube *demonstration*
77 The Blue Danube *backing only*
78 Oh! Susannah *demonstration*
79 Oh! Susannah *backing only*
80 Song Of The Volga Boatmen *demonstration*
81 Song Of The Volga Boatmen *backing only*
82 Mango Walk *demonstration*
83 Mango Walk *backing only*
84 The Entertainer
85 Enharmonic Blues *demonstration*
86 Enharmonic Blues *backing only*
87 La Forza del Destino
88 Hail The Conquering Hero
89 William Tell Overture
90 Little Brown Jug *demonstration*
91 Little Brown Jug *backing only*
92 Joshua Jazz *demonstration*
93 Joshua Jazz *backing only*
94 Maryland
95 The Animals Went In Two By Two
96 For He's A Jolly Good Fellow *demonstration*
97 For He's A Jolly Good Fellow *backing only*

How to use the CD

The tuning note on track 1 is concert A, which sounds the same as B on the clarinet.

After track 2, which gives an idea of how the clarinet can sound, the backing tracks are listed in the order in which they appear in the book. Look for the 🔘 symbol in the book for the relevant backing track. Where both parts of a duet are included on the CD, the top part is in the left channel, and the bottom part is in the right channel.

4 5 6 7 8 9

7/08 (166243/166244)